# TWO LEFT FEET

For Stuart Dalgleish
whose big smile and down-hill racing
I borrowed (without asking).
And also for John Deakin,
friend and teacher,
with love.
*Jenny Sullivan*

For Delyth, my wife,
Joseff, my son,
and thank you to
John, my friend.
*Graham Howells*

Revised edition published in 2006 by Pont Books, an imprint of
Gomer Press, Llandysul, Ceredigion, SA44 4JL

First impression - 1999
ISBN 1 84323594 3
ISBN-13 9781843235941
A CIP record for this title is available from the British Library.

© Copyright text: Jenny Sullivan
© Copyright illustrations: Graham Howells

The author and illustrator assert their moral right under the
Copyright, Designs and Patents Act, 1988
to be identified respectively as author and illustrator of this work.

Printed and bound in Wales at
Gomer Press, Llandysul, Ceredigion

# Two Left Feet

Jenny Sullivan

Graham Howells

PONT

Bryn loved school.

He loved the busy-
busy-busy sounds,
and playing with
the other
children, and
the dressing-up
corner with
all the
silly hats.

Even though he loved school, sometimes
he got cross, because he had wonky legs,
which meant he couldn't run very fast and
had to use a special frame with wheels to
help him to walk.

His dad made him laugh, because he said
that Bryn had two left feet.

When he went down the hill to the school
(but not when Mam was watching)
he liked to take his feet off the ground
and whizz down, very fast.

Bryn had lots of friends, and when they played football,

Bryn nearly always went in goal, because he was very good at saving goals.

Everyone said so, except Owain.

Owain was mad about sports. He would play every position himself if he could—goalie, striker, the lot! And when Owain picked the teams, Bryn often got left out.

Bryn had a helper-friend, Bethan, who looked after him and helped him in school. Sometimes, when Owain chose someone else for goal, Bethan cheered Bryn up by singing silly songs that soon had him smiling again.

To tell the truth, that was the very first thing that everybody noticed about Bryn – not his feet, but his great big smile! If you met him, you'd have to smile right back, because it was that sort of face.

The village where Bryn lived
was quite small, but it had something
not many other villages had – a castle.
The castle was across a busy road and up
a steep hill, but Bryn could see it from his
bedroom window. It was his favourite
view.

One day Mr Deakin's class and some helping mums went to visit the castle as a special treat. All the children walked up the hill, except Bryn, who rode up in Mr Deakin's car. He waved at the children as they drove past, and smiled his big smile.

The castle was huge, with two big turrets, one each side of an arched gateway, and most of it didn't have any roof, and was open to the sky. The place was full of birds: pigeons squabbled on the walls, and bright yellow wagtails and black and white magpies fluttered from ruined wall to arrow slit. Bryn looked up and saw a big brown buzzard riding on the wind.

Best of all there was a moat with five fat, noisy ducks swimming in it, and hundreds of orange and black goldfish glinting in amongst the weed. Their round mouths made "O" shapes on the water.

Mr Deakin showed Bryn and the other children where the people who had built the castle, hundreds and hundreds of years ago, had carved signs in the stone.

Bryn ran his finger across the marks,
and imagined what the person who
had put them there had been like.

Right in the middle of the castle was a staircase up the Great Tower, with dozens of winding stairs. They were very steep. Mr Deakin ruffled Bryn's hair.

"I don't think we can get you up there, Bryn, old son. The stairs are too dangerous. You wait in the sunshine, and we'll come back and get you afterwards."

Bryn watched the other children stream through the doorway into the tower.

He heard their excited voices as they began the climb. He stared down at his wonky legs and his two left feet. Usually he didn't mind, but today he would love to have gone to the top of that tall, tall tower.

One by one children popped out at the top of the tower and waved to Bryn. Sam, Nia, Aled.

Not Owain, though.
Mr Deakin brought him back down.
Owain's face was white and he stared
down at his feet miserably.

"Afraid of heights, eh?" said
Mr Deakin. "My brother was
exactly the same."

When all the children were down they were allowed to wander round by themselves.

"No climbing on the ruins!" Mr Deakin said sternly. "And no misbehaving."

Bethan and the mums went to look in the castle shop, and Bryn was left alone.

He stared at the doorway to the tower. He could manage the stairs at home, if he took care. No one was watching. As fast as he could, using his frame, he went to the foot of the stairs and looked up. Deep grooves had been worn in the stone steps by all the feet that had climbed them for hundreds of years.

Bryn hid his walking frame inside the door, took a deep breath and began to climb. It was very hard work, but there was an iron rail to hold on to, and step by step Bryn climbed up and up the tower. Halfway up, he was so tired that he had to stop for a rest. He waited until he got his breath back, then he climbed up and up some more.

His two left feet ached, and he didn't think he'd ever been so tired in his life. But then, at last, he arrived at the top of the tower.

The wind whipped his straight brown hair until it stood up on end. He looked around him. He could see for miles and miles: the church in the village below, the cars on the busy road, even as far as the Brecon Beacons, blue and misty in the distance. It was wonderful.

He peered over the walls at the place where he'd been sitting. It was a long, long way down. All the children, the mums and Mr Deakin were standing in a group. They looked like little black beetles from up here. Bryn cupped his hands around his mouth, and shouted as loud as he could.

"Hey! I'm up here!"

"I climbed all the way up on my two left feet! Come on up, Owain. It's great up here!"

Owain stared up. He shook his head, slowly. Then Mr Deakin whispered something in his ear.

This time, Owain nodded.

Together, Mr Deakin and Owain climbed the tower. Bryn could hear Mr Deakin's voice counting off the steps as they climbed up and up.

Soon Owain's head popped out of the stairway, and Mr Deakin (who was a bit red and puffing after climbing the winding stairs twice in one afternoon) stood right at the top of the tower with Bryn.

Bryn looked at Owain.
Owain looked at Bryn. Then they both looked over the battlements at everyone below, and waved.

Going down was much easier for Bryn, although his legs were very tired, so half way down Mr Deakin picked him up and carried him the rest of the way piggy-back. Outside the tower door, he stood him on his own two left feet.

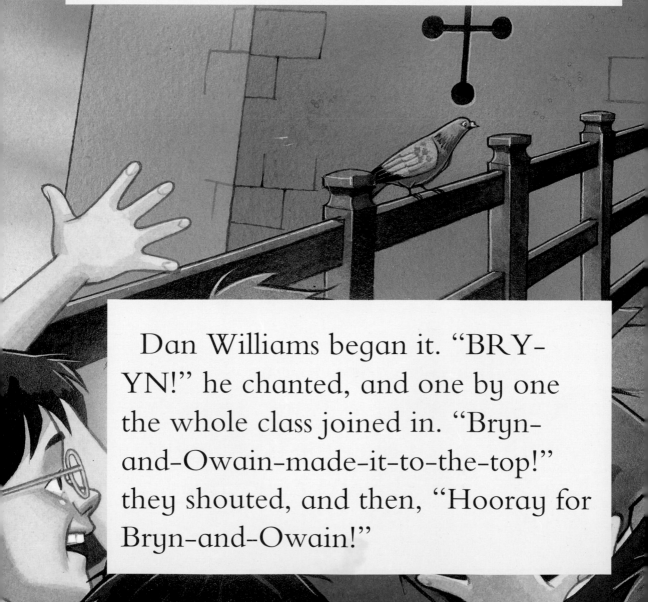

Dan Williams began it. "BRY-YN!" he chanted, and one by one the whole class joined in. "Bryn-and-Owain-made-it-to-the-top!" they shouted, and then, "Hooray for Bryn-and-Owain!"

"We made it to the top, Owain!" said Bryn.

"We did, didn't we?"

And Bryn smiled his great, big smile.